publishers
PAUL ENS and SCOTT CHITWOOD

graphic design
PAUL ENS

BODIE TROLL Volume One

This volume collects BODIE TROLL #1 through #4 of the comic-book series originally printed by Red 5 Comics.

Published by
RED 5 COMICS
298 Tuscany Vista Rd NW, Calgary, Alberta, Canada, T3L 3B4

www.red5comics.com

To find a comics shop in your area, call the Comic Shop Locator Service toll-free at 1-888-266-4226

First edition:
ISBN-13: 978-0-9868985-7-0

Printed in Canada.

**SCRIPT AND ART**
**JAY FOSGITT**

**COLORS**
**JAY FOSGITT**
**EVAN SHANER** (ISSUE 1 PAGES 1-4)
**JAY JACOT** (ISSUES 3-4)

WWW.RED5COMICS.COM

# Introduction, By Alyson Court

Cute. It's a four letter word. The four letter C-word that was the bane throughout my childhood. Being wee--easily 2/3 the size of any classmate--freckled and chubby cheeked often gave outsiders the impression that I was an angelic little darling. Occasionally they'd even manage to maintain this misconception, so long as I kept a sock in my mouth. Usually, though, it was my foot.

Yup, being called "cute" by pretty much any and everyone--blech. It was awful. That is, until I found my calling in showbiz! Suddenly being ten years old but looking six had a positive side. Soon I was on TV and film screens across the continent, dancing and singing my adorable little tush off. But not only did I look young, I sounded young too and quickly landed my first role in an animated series, as Malani in Nelvana's "Ewoks".

Since that first voice job, I've had the opportunity to voice hundreds of characters, many of them iconic. I've also had the fortune to work with many of our industry's top illustrators, writers and animators, as well as meeting up and coming cartoonists ever eager to share their work. And so it was that I came to meet Bodie. Well, technically I met his creator, Jay Fosgitt, but that was simply a conduit introduction to The Troll.

In "Bodie Troll", Jay's imagination takes the reader to places completely unexpected, and his visual style conjures many of the great European cartoonists--from Uderzo to Morris, with a suave dash of Disney for good measure, all blended into something uniquely his own. The writing is unpredictably funny, full of humor that will tickle young and old alike.

I instantly fell in love with Bodie. If we're being honest, there's probably more than a little kindred spirit at play here, as Bodie's irreverent sass and grumpy wit are juxtaposed with an utterly adorable design, much to the chagrin of a troll whose sole desire is to be feared. Sadly, no matter the trouble Bodie manages to create, he simply ends up smothered in hugs and kisses (which, upon further reflection, is rather a fittingly harsh punishment for a troll after all).

So prepare to laugh, then duck and run for cover as the next giant penny drops. There's no predicting what will happen in Bodie's world and, well, Bodie is just so gosh darned cute. But you didn't hear that from me!

---

Known for her portrayal of such iconic characters as Loonette the Clown from the children's show "The Big Comfy Couch", Claire Redfield from the video game "Resident Evil", Jubilee from the "X-Men" cartoon, and Lydia from the "Beetlejuice" cartoon, **Alyson Court** can currently be heard as Queen Martha in "Mike The Knight" and as Trina in "Grojband". She continues to perform both on and off camera, in addition to writing, producing and directing children's television, animation, film and video games.

GOOD GRAVY, MIZ BIJOU! YOU ABOUT SCARED ME OUTTA MY **FUR**!!

*PAK!*

I OUGHTA KNOCK YOU OUTTA IT! REMEMBER THAT CRATE OF EGGS YOU WERE GONNA PICK UP FOR ME FROM DUCKSBREATH HOLLOW?

YEAH, SO? I GOT 'EM TO YA...

EVENTUALLY.

THEY WERE **HATCHED**!

SO NOW YOU GOT CHICKENS TO MAKE MORE EGGS! THAT'S MORE THAN YOU BARGAINED FOR! I DESERVE A **BONUS**!

HERE'S YOUR BREAKFAST, BODIE!

...BUT I'LL GLADLY ACCEPT MY STANDARD PAYMENT OF ALL THE ROOTS I CAN EAT!

NOTHING DOING, CHOLLY!

BODIE'S GOTTA EARN HIS KEEP, AND UNTIL HE DOES...

...I EAT HIS ROOTS!

HEY! NO FAIR!!

YOU ROLLED THESE ON THE FLOOR, DIDN'T YOU?

AW MAN, THEY SMELL RIPE, TOO...

*KRUMP!*

Hey, Hunk!

HEARD YOU'VE GOT A BIG FAT EGG!

DO I EVER, BODIE! CHICKEN THAT LAID 'ER MUST BE ON CRUTCHES!

CAN'T IMAGINE WHAT IT WAS DOING OUT IN SANDERS' FIELD WHERE I FOUND 'ER!

SANDERS' FIELD? DIDN'T I JUST HEAR SOMETHING ABOUT THAT PLACE...?

HEY! YOU GOT A HORSE!

RAR! RAR! BLEHR! BLARG!!

I CAN'T EVEN SCARE AN UP-SIDE DOWN HORSE!

ABOUT MY EGG..?

OH, YEAH.

WELL, I'M HOPING THESE ... UM... FIVE CLINKERS BIJOU GAVE ME WILL COVER IT...

HECK BODIE, I'LL GIVE YOU THREE IF YOU CAN LUG IT OFF YOURSELF!

WITH MIZ BIJOU'S CLINKERS, THAT'LL GIMME FIFTEEN— ENOUGH TO BUY MYSELF A WHOLE ROOT GARDEN...

'COURSE, IF MIZ BIJOU FOUND OUT, SHE'D KILL ME...

I KEPT 'ER FRESH IN THE BEST PLACE I KNEW HOW— RIGHT ATOP MY FORGE!

YOU KEEP FOOD FRESH ABOVE AN OPEN FLAME? I'D HATE TO SEE HOW YOU STORE YOUR MILK!

THE SAME WAY! I LIKE MY DAIRY CHEWY!

THEN THEY CAN BURY ME IN MY SPIFFY NEW ROOT GARDEN!

HUNK, LET ME AT THAT CHUNKY HEN FRUIT!

AW, NOT ANOTHER HATCHING!

BIJOU'S GONNA EAT ME ALIVE!!

HEADS UP, BODIE! THAT BIG VARMINT MAY DO IT FIRST!!

MAN ALIVE, WHAT A BUTT-UGLY CHICKEN!

SNIFF SNIFF... YOU SMELL THAT? IT'S KINDA LIKE...

CHROK! CHROK!

BOILED GOAT'S MILK! AND WHERE THERE'S GOAT'S MILK, THERE'S GOATS!

DON'T EVEN THINK ABOUT IT, BUSTER...

SCARING GOATS IS MY THING!

THIS HERE'S THE LAST OF THE GOAT'S MILK. BETTER CALL IN THE HERD FROM SANDERS' FIELD.

AND WHERE'S THAT EGG BODIE WAS FETCHING FOR ME?

I THINK THE EGG IS FETCHING BODIE...

HUH?!

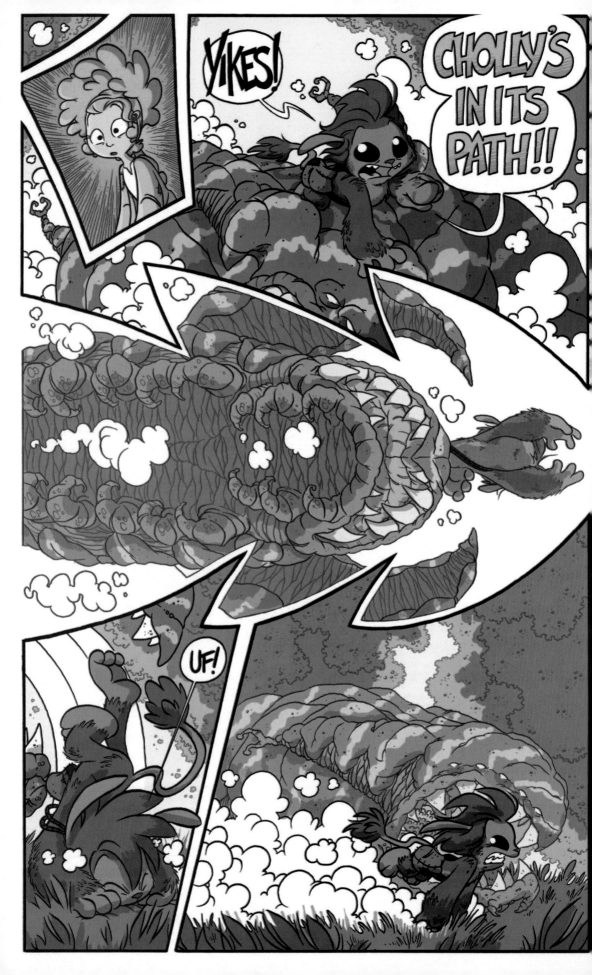

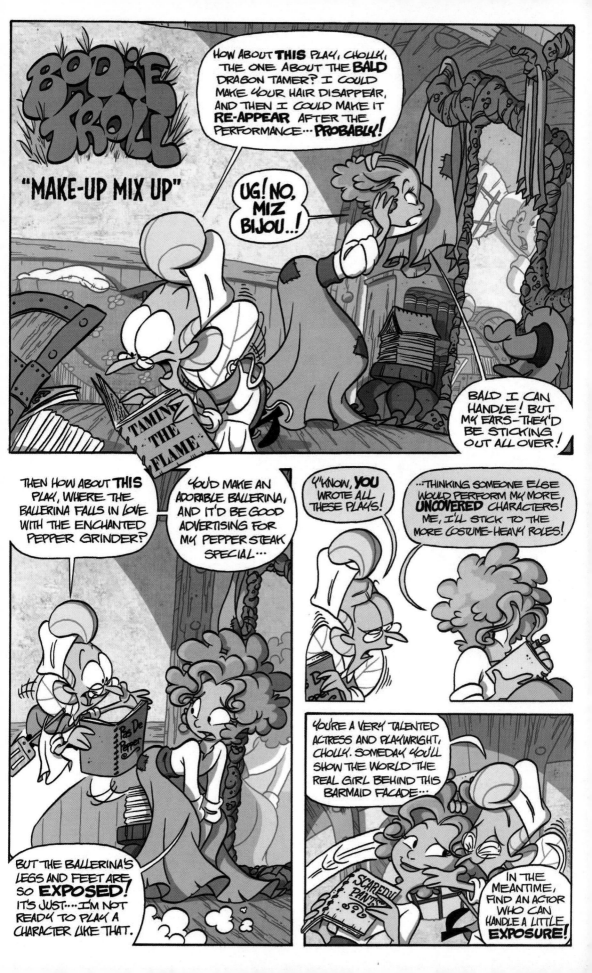

...AND JUST A BIT OF LIPSTICK WILL MAKE YOUR KISSER **POP!**

**FUMP!**

"FUZZY MUG?!"

NOW GET OUT THERE AND MAKE THEATRE FANS OUTTA MY CUSTOMERS!

**CLAP CLAP CLAP CLAP CLAP** CLAP CLAP

Y'KNOW, TROLL FACES ARE **SUPPOSED** TO BE FUZZY! WHAT'S **YOUR** EXCUSE, LADY?!

LATER IN THE THIRD ACT...

OH, MY POOR PRINCE GARETH! THE DOG WITCH OF LOCH ROON HAS TRANSFORMED YOU INTO A HIDEOUS CREATURE!

WATCH IT WITH THE "HIDEOUS" TALK...

I MUSTA DONE A HECKUVA JOB OUT THERE! YOU HEAR THAT APPLAUSE?!

LET'S GO BACK OUT THERE AND REDO THE ENDING— BUT THIS TIME, I'LL BREAK INTO A WICKED LUTE SOLO!

CLAPCLA
CLAPCLA
CLAPCLA
CLAPCLA
P

LEMME JUST MAKE SURE...

MY FUR LOOKS...

...OKAY?

THIS AIN'T THE FACE I STARTED ACT THREE WITH, CHOLLY!!

WHAT'D I DO, MIZ BIJOU?!

QUICK— KISS HIM BEFORE HE HAS A HISSY FIT MELTDOWN!

?!

"WISHY WASHY"...

"STINKIN' RICH"...

AFTER THE SHOW...

GRUMBLE GRUMBLE GRUMBLE...

I'M THE ONE WHO HAD TO KISS **MANURE**!!

OH, QUIT YOUR BELLYACHING, BODIE...

WELL, YOU CAN KISS YOUR CO-STAR GOODBYE! NO MORE STUPID TRANSFORMATIONS FOR **THIS** TROLL!

OH NO—BODIE, **PLEASE**! I CAN'T DO THIS WITHOUT **YOU**!

THEN HOW 'BOUT I KISS **YOU** WITH THIS KOOKY LIPSWITCH, AND THEN **YOU** CAN PLAY A TALKING PILE OF POO!

BUF!

BODIE, I—

FDUMP

?

YOU'RE STILL...

YOU?

HOW COME IT DIDN'T WORK?

I GUESS… I DUNNO…

I'M JUST AS TRANSFORMED AS I'M GONNA GET.

WELL, WHAT'S THAT MEAN?!

NOTHING, OKAY?! THERE'S JUST SOMETHING WRONG WITH ME! ALWAYS HAS BEEN, ALWAYS WILL BE!!!

I'LL JUST TELL MIZ BIJOU THAT THE DINNER SHOWS ARE CANCELLED. SO JUST FORGET IT…

CHOLLY..?

I DON'T THINK THERE'S ANYTHING WRONG WITH YOU. I JUST DIDN'T KISS YOU GOOD.

IT'S MY FAULT.

I WANNA KEEP PLAYIN' YOUR CHARACTERS.

PLEASE?

EVEN IF IT'S WORSE THAN TALKING POO?

NOTHING'S WORSE THAN TALKING POO…

KUNK

ER...

SEEMS A SEAT JUST OPENED UP.

IS IT INTERMISSION YET..?!

YOU **DO** TRY MY PATIENCE, BODIE— BUT I APPRECIATE YOU HELPING CHOLLY...

AW, I'D DO ANYTHING FOR CHOLLY, MIZ BIJOU...

EVEN SUFFER THROUGH PUKEY GIRL KISSES.

PICKLEBERRY WINE

ROOTS

BY THE WAY— WHY DIDN'T THE LIPSWITCH TRANSFORM CHOLLY WHEN **I** KISSED **HER**?

OH, UM... IT MUST'VE BEEN YOUR FURRY FACE. THE LIPSWITCH COULDN'T STICK TO ALL THAT FUZZ.

SURE. THAT'LL DO.

ALMOST SHOW TIME! READY FOR YOUR 'BIG CHANGE', BODIE?

READY AS I'M GETTIN'. THIS IS THE WORST YOU'VE ASKED OF ME YET!

I OWE YOU BIG TIME, SWEETIE...

SMEK...

FSSSSSSSS!

AW MAN, YOU EVEN HAVE ME SMELLIN' LIKE STUPID FLOWERS!

IT BEATS YOUR USUAL 'DAMP FUR AND DIRT' MUSK!

DON'T START, LADY! I CAN PUNCH A GIRL NOW THAT I AM ONE!!

SHOWTIME, "BODETTE"!

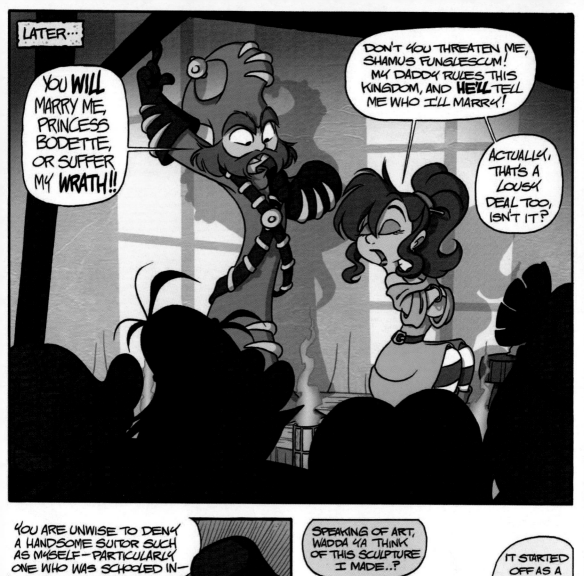

YOU WEAR THE SPOILED, STUBBORN SKIN OF A PRINCESS...

GOTCHA!

YOU'VE CHEWED UP ALL THE LIPSWITCH!!

RUB RUB RUB RUB RUB RUB RUB RUB RUB RUB RUB RUB RUB

LET'S HOPE THIS STILL WORKS...

ME FIRST!! ME FIRST!!

FDUMP!

SMEK♥

PAF!

?!

IT WORKED! I'M A **DUDE** AGAIN!!

I'M SO HAPPY, I COULD WRITE MY NAME IN THE SNOW!

COULD YA KISS MIZ BIJOU INTO A PILE OF SNOW?!

BODIE!

A STRANGER ON **MY** BRIDGE?! THAT'S MY **CUE!**

PFV!

CAN I GET SOME OF THAT TASTY GOOP TO GO?

HUH-HUH-HUH... BEWARE... TRESS **CHOKE!** PASSER... **GUH!** TERRIBLE MONSTER... **HOO!** SO SKUH-SCARY... HIHNH! YOU SHUH-SHALL... NOT... **PUH!** PASS...

...OUT FROM EXHAUSTION...

PUMBT!

OH, I SEE! YOU MUST BE A WICKED KOBOLD, AND I MUST GUESS YOUR NAME, OR ELSE GIVE YOU SOMETHING PRECIOUS TO ME!

HUH?! I'M NO KOBOLD!

THEY STEAL BABIES AND SMELL LIKE ONION BURPS!

IIIIIIS YOUR NAAAAAME...

FRANCINE?

NO, OF COURSE NOT! WHO EVER HEARD OF A KOBOLD NAMED FRANCINE?!

OH WELL! LOOKS LIKE I LOSE, AND YOU WIN MY BABY!

SEE YA!

SOON...

THRUMM'S Dry Goods

SORRY, BODIE...

I JUST BUY DRY GOODS... NOT BABIES.

MAYBE I'LL TRADE 'EM TO GUSTAV FOR SOME MORE GOOP...

THE SOCKO REPORT! PRINT EDITION WEATHER REPORT STILL NO RAIN

SOUP STONES 3¢ PER POUND

SINGING BONES

WHERE'D HE COME FROM?

WHAT'RE YOU, LIKE A THOUSAND YEARS OLD? YOU OUGHTA KNOW WHERE BABIES COME FROM!

DO YOU?

SURE, I DO...!

"THERE'S A VILLAGE TEN MILES WEST OF HERE THAT GROWS 'EM IN AN OLD SPITTOON FILLED WITH GROUND UP JELLYBEANS AND UNICORN BOOGERS!" EVERYBODY KNOWS THAT!"

SOUNDS ABOUT RIGHT.

Hey!

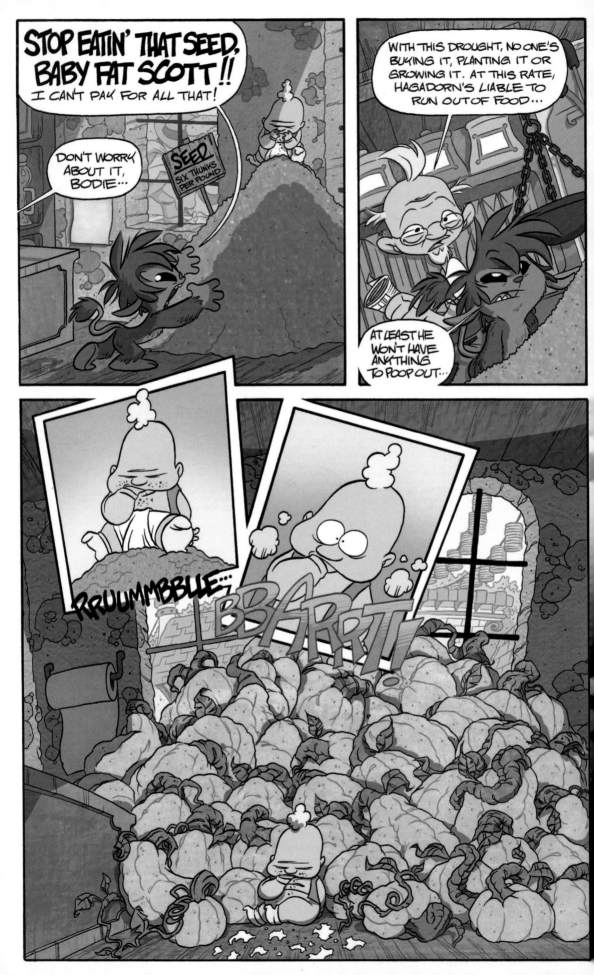

THINK YOU COULD STEW UP A SACK OF ROOTS FOR ME, CHOLLY?

WE HAVEN'T ANY WATER FOR STEWING, THANKS TO THE DROUGHT.

GOT ANY MOLDY BREAD FOR A ROOT SANDWICH?

SURE! I EVEN HAVE SOME RANCID MAYO TO GO WITH IT!

NOW **THAT'S** GOOD EATIN'! LEMME JUST... GRAB ME... SOME... UM...

PPRROOT

GIMME A ROOT SANDWICH, HOLD THE ROOTS...

MMMOOOOOOOOOOOOO
THUNK!

IS THAT A... **COW** ON THE ROOF?

BUDDABUDDABUH-

MMOOOOOO..!
BUMF!

NOT ANYMORE!

**BODIE TROLL!**

**IT AIN'T MY COW, LADY!!**

WHAT COW? I'M HERE FOR YOUR WHEELBARROW!

SORRY. I'M USED TO GETTING BLAMED FOR STUFF.

IT'S USUALLY YOUR FAULT!

GET TO THE POINT!

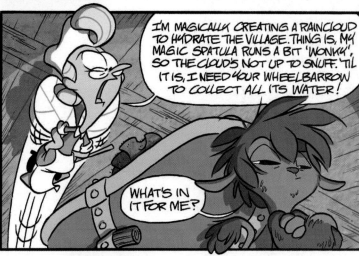

I'M MAGICALLY CREATING A RAINCLOUD TO HYDRATE THE VILLAGE. THING IS, MY MAGIC SPATULA RUNS A BIT 'WONKY', SO THE CLOUD'S NOT UP TO SNUFF. 'TIL IT IS, I NEED YOUR WHEELBARROW TO COLLECT ALL ITS WATER!

WHAT'S IN IT FOR ME?

BESIDES **NOT** DYING OF THIRST? IT'S **YOUR** FAULT MY WASHTUB HAS A HOLE IN IT, FORCING ME TO USE YOUR WHEELBARROW!

**YOU** ZAPPED THE TUB WITH YOUR MAGIC SPATULA TRYIN' TO GET **ME**, YA PSYCHO!!

BECAUSE **YOU** BLEW UP A MONSTER IN MY KITCHEN WITH YOUR **PEE**, YA NIMROD!

OKAY, I'M LOST NOW. WHERE WERE WE?

YOU WERE ABOUT TO LEND ME YOUR WHEELBARROW FOR MY RAINCLOUD.

REALLY? THAT'S NICE OF ME. NORMALLY I'M MORE OF A JERK...

IT'D BE A *LOT* EASIER TO STEER THIS TUB WITHOUT THAT TWO-TON DIAPER YOU'RE SPORTIN'...

I DON'T CARE ABOUT THE CLOUD. I JUST HOPE THEY'RE OKAY.

I ADMIT— IF BODIE SURVIVES THIS, I MIGHT JUST CONSIDER NOT KILLING HIM.

SPLUD!!!

NOPE.

STILL GONNA KILL HIM.

SKREE-FOP!

NO GOOD...!

I'LL SAY **THIS** ABOUT THE WEATHER...

IT DRIES YOUR HAIR AT THE DROP OF A **HAT!**

FUMP!

BUFFFFF...

OR THE DROP OF A **TROLL!**

UH, I RETURNED THE KID TO THE BABY-DELIVERING HARPY THAT DROPPED HIM! THEY FLEW OFF TO THE POPCORN ISLANDS, WHERE HE WAS ADOPTED BY REFORMED PIRATES WHO GAVE UP PILLAGING IN FAVOR OF BLOWING ZERBERTS ON BABIES' TUMMIES!

I THOUGHT BABIES WERE GROWN IN SPITTOONS...?

OH, GROW UP! THIS MAKES WAY MORE SENSE!

BODIE, WHAT THE HAIRY HECK IS GOIN' ON...?

BA-BROOOM!!

THE DROUGHT HAS ENDED!!

I CAN WASH THE POOP FRUIT TASTE OUTTA MY MOUTH!

HEY, WHO VOTES THAT WE FORGET ALL ABOUT OMNIPOTENT BABIES, KOBOLDS, AND MAGICAL POOP, AND JUST BE GLAD THAT THE RAIN HAS RETURNED?!

I AIN'T CONVINCED THAT YER NOT BEHIND ALL THIS, BODIE.

BUT I AIN'T CONVINCED THAT'S A BAD THING, EITHER.

TAP TAP TAP

KEEP YER STUPID SECRETS.

I KNOW YOU WANT FOLKS TO FEAR YOU, BODIE. BUT DESPITE IT ALL, YOU'RE A HERO, WHETHER THEY KNOW IT OR NOT. I HOPE YOU CAN LIVE WITH THAT.

I KNOW I CAN.

THE END!

I never throw away an idea. My sketchbooks are filled with story concepts and doodles that were either intended for a project that got cut short, or never happened at all. That leaves me with a scrap yard of creativity to cobble together for whole other purposes. That is exactly how "Bodie Troll" came to be, though it took thirteen years to happen...

# BODIE BEGINNINGS
## PART 1: COLLEGE COMICS

THE EPIC OF CHOLLY by Jay P. Fosgitt

In 2000, I was in college and working on my school paper as staff cartoonist. I'd created a comic called "The Epic of Cholly", about a girl in college. But my goal was to draw a syndicated comic strip that would be seen in papers worldwide. At that time, syndicated cartoonist Greg Evans ("Luann") gave me some sound advice: The age 50 and up readership that sustained newspapers wouldn't read a comic about college students. That was fine with me. I didn't want to draw them.

I'd been a fan of fairy tales all my life. So I decided to draw a strip like "Wizard of Id" and "Hagar the Horrible"--silly, anachronistic takes on the genre. Sitting in a diner one night, I scribbled the design below on a placemat of a barmaid, whom I imagined as the star of the strip.

I began to sketch random fairy tale archetypes-- kings, queens, princes, poets, wizards, dragons, warriors--just to play around with designs and see if any real characters would spring to life. Some of these sketches were based on older ideas I'd created, and others would end up being used for future projects.

As I developed the concept, I kept going back to my old "Cholly" cast as character templates. After awhile, it hit me that the "Cholly" characters fit so well that they should *be* the characters. Things really started clicking once that choice was made.

Cholly would become my barmaid (as well as an aspiring writer) and the comic strip's central character. The name Cholly came from my grandpa Bill, who had nicknamed me Cholly when I was a little kid.

In my college strip, Miz Bijou was Cholly's aunt. In this new strip, Miz Bijou became Cholly's fairy godmother, and the proprietor of The Drunken Pumpkin tavern. Bijou's establishment was almost called The Sandhill Tavern, after the bar my grandpa Bill's dad founded in the 1930's.

The one fantasy element to carry over was a grumpy little monster (sound familiar?) named Gunk. Gunk used to be Cholly's childhood imaginary friend who followed her to college. For this new strip, he would become a Rumplestiltskin-type character. Cholly had guessed his name, so Gunk became her servant.

I decided the title "The Epic of Cholly" fit a fairy tale comic nicely, so it stayed. Here is the first (and only) strip that I drew for my new "Epic of Cholly"...

FAERIES ARE A DAINTY FOLK...

THEY GRANT WISHES WHENEVER THEY'RE SPOTTED...

BUT WHAT'S NEATEST OF ALL, THAT I CAN RECALL...

...THEY MAKE SQUOOSHY NOISES WHEN SWATTED.

SHE GOT BILL!

CLAP FOR ME, GUYS... COUGH WHEEZE

I showed this sample to Greg Evans. He liked it, but gave me another bit of wisdom: "Hagar the Horrible wouldn't sell today." He saw anachronistic fairy tale comics as cliche and old fashioned, and imagined newspaper syndicate editors would, too. So I took his advice, and shelved the comic. Maybe newspaper syndicates *would* find my concept hokey, I thought. But then again, maybe newspapers weren't where "The Epic of Cholly" belonged...

# BODIE BEGINNINGS
## PART 2: THE QUACKING DEAD

By 2008, I still had fairy tales on the brain. I had just landed a publisher to release my graphic novel, "Dead Duck". The book was about a duck-minion of death who delivered the dead with his sidekick, Zombie Chick. And though the stories took place in various environments, many of them occurred in medieval villages or featured fairy tale archetypes. It was obvious where my true interests lay.

One day, as I sketched other minions for Dead Duck to work with, this face came out of my pen. I never wound up using the design in "Dead Duck", but I held onto it (as I always do), figuring I'd find a place for that face someday...

By 2010, "Dead Duck" was released, and I met "Hellboy" creator Mike Mignola. Mike liked "Dead Duck, and I liked "Hellboy", so I got inspired to write and draw a two-page story from Hellboy's youth. Mike's character designs were already established, but for the story I wrote, I needed to design a girl troll. This little scribble to the right was the only one I needed to do before I knew I had the character.

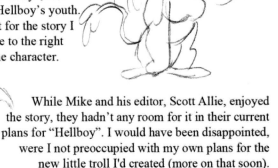

While Mike and his editor, Scott Allie, enjoyed the story, they hadn't any room for it in their current plans for "Hellboy". I would have been disappointed, were I not preoccupied with my own plans for the new little troll I'd created (more on that soon).

You can read my never-before-seen kid Hellboy story in this volume, published here with the permission of "Hellboy" creator Mike Mignola.

# BODIE BEGINNINGS
## PART 3: A TROLL IS BORN

I really liked my new troll character, and wanted to use it for something. My thoughts went back to my unused "Epic of Cholly" concept, which seemed like a perfect start. But instead of Cholly being the main character, I really wanted the comic to be about the troll--making him both the star, and the comic relief.

Here is the first "post-Hellboy story" drawing I did of my troll. The design got a little modified, making the troll stubbier and cuter. I went back and forth on whether to make it a girl or boy, and as of this design, I deemed my troll a male. The decision was made based on the heavily-female cast that I was already developing. The troll was also taking on a lot of my own personality quirks, so writing him as a boy just made more sense. To the right are names I scrawled out in my sketch book before settling on the best one.

JIM? HENNY? CHOKKO?
EGGER? EDGAR?
NEED SOMETHING SHARP
AND SIMPLE. ONE SYLLABLE
BINK. BIP. POP. FLRNK.
BUNK. GUNK. TUNK.
SCRUFF. PUNK. SHOOP. TRIP.
SCRAP. FLECK.
SPLUDGE. SMUDGE.
BASIL? GOOCHER?
BOOG? BASHER?
BASH? BODIE?
BODIE TROLL?

Once I chose Bodie for his name, the character was basically all there. The following sketches show me experimenting with Bodie's body language and facial expressions.

Cholly went through a number of changes before her character was completely established...

My original idea was to make Cholly a little girl, as well as the keeper of the pigs for Miz Bijou...

I made Cholly older again, but switched up her look with a pointy nose...

I tried out a look for her that included bangs and big feet...

To the right, you can see different spellings that I tried, even considering naming her after Wendy in "Peter Pan"...

I tried giving Cholly a short skirt and buccaneer boots...

CHOLLY
CHOLLIE
WENDY
CHALLIE
CHOLEE

Miz Bijou's character went through several developments as well...

THUP
THUP
THUP

MIZ BIJOU
GRANNY
BASTIAN

I thought of changing her name to Granny Bastian, after my friend, artist Jeremy Bastian.

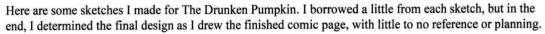

Here are some sketches I made for The Drunken Pumpkin. I borrowed a little from each sketch, but in the end, I determined the final design as I drew the finished comic page, with little to no reference or planning.

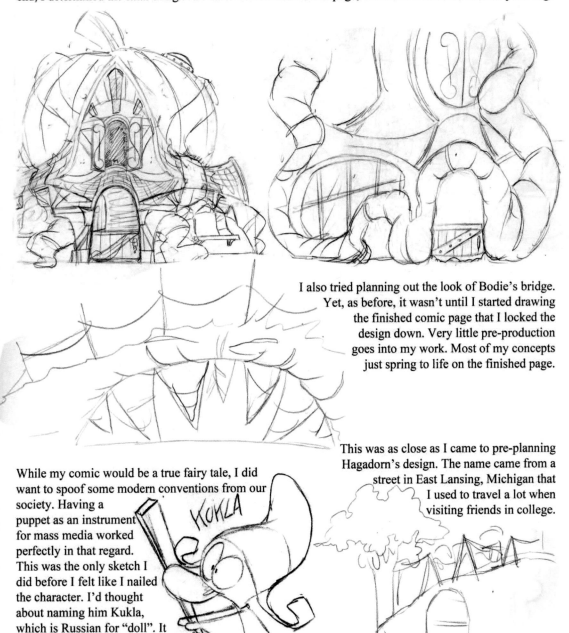

I also tried planning out the look of Bodie's bridge. Yet, as before, it wasn't until I started drawing the finished comic page that I locked the design down. Very little pre-production goes into my work. Most of my concepts just spring to life on the finished page.

This was as close as I came to pre-planning Hagadorn's design. The name came from a street in East Lansing, Michigan that I used to travel a lot when visiting friends in college.

While my comic would be a true fairy tale, I did want to spoof some modern conventions from our society. Having a puppet as an instrument for mass media worked perfectly in that regard. This was the only sketch I did before I felt like I nailed the character. I'd thought about naming him Kukla, which is Russian for "doll". It was also the name of a famous puppet from the 1950's. Inspired by the classic English puppet, Punch, I came up with a similar name for my character, and thus, Socko was born.

Once I'd established the characters and locations, the overall story of "Bodie Troll" quickly unfolded. With only four pages of issue #1 completed, I showed my samples to Red 5 Comics. They took an immediate interest in "Bodie Troll", and within a couple of months, my comic found its publisher, and my thirteen-year-long dream of creating my own fairy tale finally came true.

# TROLLING FOR BABES

By Jay P. Fosgitt

NORWAY, 1947...

GONNA SEE A TROLL, GONNA SEE A TROLL, NANANANANOONYNAY, I'M GONNA SEE A TROLL...!

CALM YOURSELF, HELLBOY...

THE LAST TROLL SIGHTING IN NORWAY WAS IN 1915, AND THAT TURNED OUT TO BE A TUMOROUS PIG!

GASP!

I WANNA SEE A TUMOROUS PIG!!

SIGH...

MUCH AS I VALUE OUR SHARED APPRECIATION OF THE OCCULT, I SOMETIMES WISH YOU HELD INTERESTS MORE COMMON TO A YOUNG BOY...

LIKE GIRLS!

BLEH!

GIRLS ARE ICKY! I'D RATHER KISS A TUMOROUS PIG!

YOU MAY GET YOUR CHANCE.

NOW, STAY PUT WHILE I GET US SOME LUNCH.

UH!

LUNSJ

DON'T EVEN MENTION "PAMCAKES".

NOW, HOW DO YOU LIKE YOUR FERMENTED TROUT?

WITH EXTRA PAMCAKES.

POK!

HEY!

# DRAWING A CROWD
## POPULATING BODIE'S WORLD

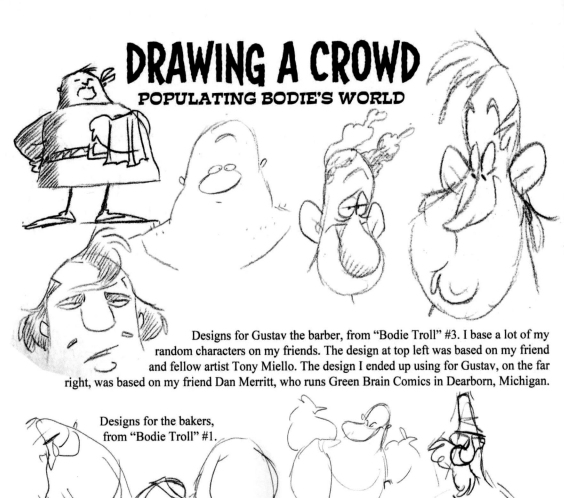

Designs for Gustav the barber, from "Bodie Troll" #3. I base a lot of my random characters on my friends. The design at top left was based on my friend and fellow artist Tony Miello. The design I ended up using for Gustav, on the far right, was based on my friend Dan Merritt, who runs Green Brain Comics in Dearborn, Michigan.

Designs for the bakers, from "Bodie Troll" #1.

Designs for Hunkwood the Blacksmith, from "Bodie Troll" #1. He was originally going to have a scorched face from working near a hot forge.

Designs for Baby Fat Scott's parents, Scotius and Sonia, from "Bodie Troll" #4.

Designs for the washer woman in "Bodie Troll" #3.

To the right, a sketch for Baby Fat Scott. I first drew the character around 1999, as a caricature of my best friend Scott's baby picture. I used the character for several comics over the years.

KOBOLD DESIGNS

Designs for Francine the kobold, from "Bodie Troll" #3. The look I chose (above) was inspired by my old character, Gunk.

# TRADING FACES
## The many looks of Bodie Troll

Designs of Bodie in his prince costume, before and after transformation, from "Bodie Troll" #2.

A design of Bodie transformed into a couch.

Cholly, dressed as Shamus Funglescum--the man who threatens Bodette, and as the old lady who discovers her couch is an evil presence.

Bodie, as the genie of the wash tub.

Character designs for Bodie, as Tuber the Terrible.

Bodie as "Bodette". The character's look was loosely based on E.G. Daily, the actress who played Dottie in "Pee Wee's Big Adventure".

# SHAPE UP OR SHIP OUT
## Designing the W.S. Skybottom

My original idea for The Clan Nimbo's ship was a floating city. When I realized that only two people would be running it, I pared it down to a floating warehouse, filled with giant cogs and pulleys. Even that felt unwieldy for just two people to manage, so I settled on a ship, which I initially wanted to avoid. Sky ships are a commonly used device in fantasy, so the trick was to have mine be different from those that came before.

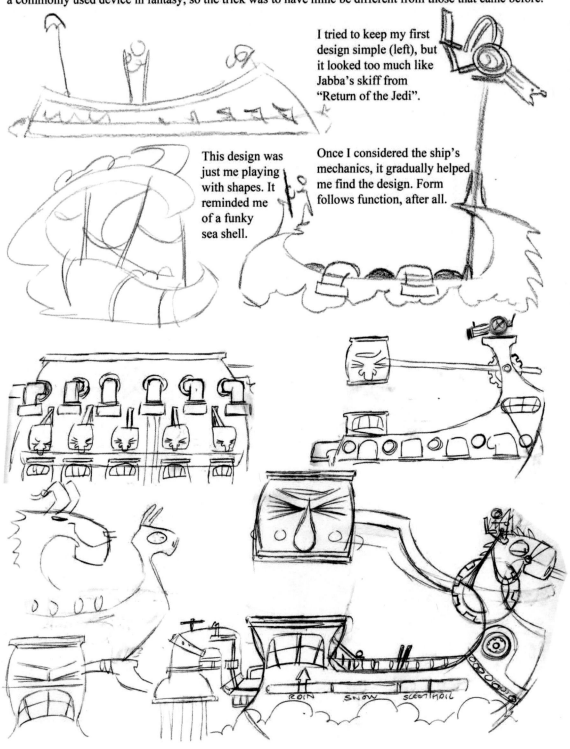

I tried to keep my first design simple (left), but it looked too much like Jabba's skiff from "Return of the Jedi".

This design was just me playing with shapes. It reminded me of a funky sea shell.

Once I considered the ship's mechanics, it gradually helped me find the design. Form follows function, after all.

RAIN     SNOW     SLEET/HAIL

# Snack Time!

# A TALE OF THANKS...

For years, I wanted to sew my own patch into the literary quilt of folk and fairy tales. I grew up with a broad appreciation of them, from the classical texts, to the Disney versions, to satirical takes seen in Jay Ward's "Fractured Fairy Tales" and Jim Henson's Muppets. I even experienced them through the oral tradition, as my grandmother would tell me folk tales that fit the classic mold, but were her own homespun creations. So, in keeping with the fairy tale theme, you could almost say is was prophesized that I'd create my own fairy tale. Least wise, the odds were pretty darn good. But nothing written in the stars or foreseen in a crystal ball would have be enough to make my fantasy a reality. Besides my own abilities and ambition, I've had so many wonderful people who helped me along the path to publishing "Bodie Troll". To those people: thank you all for clapping your hands and saying you believed in me.

**To my family,** for your love and endless support of my talent and dreams. A special mention to my late **Grandpa Bill**--without your unique childhood nickname for me, Cholly would never have come to be.

**To my friends,** for your support, suggestions, and in so many cases, for serving as supporting characters in "Bodie Troll".

**To all the artists** who contributed pin-ups to this first "Bodie Troll" mini-series. Thank you for your talent and time, and for giving me such impressive artistic heights to aspire towards.

**To Jason Hedgcock,** for booking my flight to San Diego in 2012. You got me to Comic Con, which afforded me incredible contacts and experiences, and allowed me to show "Bodie Troll" to Red 5 Comics in person. Thank you for being such an important piece to the puzzle of my success.

**To Shawna Gore,** for leading me through the dense jungle of a comic contract, and bringing me out the other side alive.

**To Evan Shaner,** for coloring the first four pages of what would eventually become "Bodie Troll" #1. Your inspired coloring made good work great, and set the standard for how I'd color "Bodie" myself from that point onward.

**To Jay Jacot,** for not only being a rapid-fire flatter on issues 2-4, but for being an amazing cheerleader for "Bodie Troll" at conventions, and for being a constant source of support and inspiration.

**To Paul and Scott of Red 5,** for taking a chance on me and "Bodie Troll", for being proactive in its promotion, and for being as giddily enthusiastic about the book's future as I am.

**To Mike Mignola and Scott Allie,** for allowing me to run my never-before-seen "Kid Hellboy" story in this collection. Your generosity helped me show my readers where Bodie began.

**To Alyson Court,** for always inspiring me with her performances, for her lovely foreword, and, when the day comes, for being the voice of Cholly.

**To my lifelong hero, Jim Henson.** Thank you for being a continual source of hope and inspiration, and for showing me at a young age that monsters could be funny and loveable.

And thank you, my readers, for making "Bodie" a success. I look forward to continuing Bodie's adventures for years to come, and having you with me at every step of the journey!